This Book
Belongs To

MONKEYS NEVER
SAY PLEASE

Written by Alice Joyce Davidson

Illustrated by Cara Marks

Text copyright © 1986 by Alice Joyce Davidson
Art copyright © 1986 by Cara Marks
Published by the C.R. Gibson Company
Norwalk, Connecticut 06856
Printed in the United States of America
ISBN 0-8378-5085-1

The C.R. Gibson Company, Norwalk, Connecticut 06856

Monkeys who live in the trees
Swing from their tails and their knees.
They play and they fight,
And they're far from polite,
For monkeys don't ever say "Please!"

But You're Not A Monkey!

Some hippos are bigger than tanks.
They don't care for laughter and pranks,
And they're not very pleasant
When they get a present.
They never say "Thank you" or "Thanks!"

But You're Not A Hippopotamus!

Lions, who live in a den,
Like to eat soup now and then.
You can tell that you're near
By the slurps that you hear
Over and over again!

But You're Not A Lion!

Octopuses who swim in the seas
Do whatever they please.
When they sit at a table,
They grab all they're able,
And never say "Please pass the peas."

**But You're Not
An Octopus!**

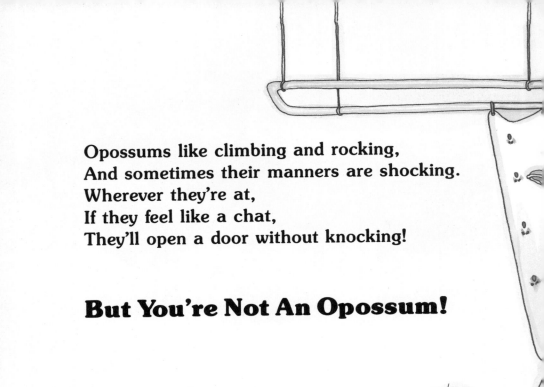

Opossums like climbing and rocking,
And sometimes their manners are shocking.
Wherever they're at,
If they feel like a chat,
They'll open a door without knocking!

But You're Not An Opossum!

Cows are often quite rude
When they're in a grass-eating mood.
They moo as they chew.
They chew as they moo.
They talk with their mouths full of food.

But You're Not A Cow!

Weasels are furry and small.
They sneak and they silently crawl.
And when weasels borrow
Some things for tomorrow,
They never return them at all!

But You're Not A Weasel!

Parrots are known for their squawking.
They squawk when they're flying and walking.
It's not their concern
To give others a turn.
A parrot just loves to keep talking!

But You're Not
A Parrot!

Rhinos are gentle and mild,
Except for the times when they're riled,
Then they'll roll on the ground
With a terrible sound.
Their tantrums are awful and wild!

But You're Not A Rhinoceros!

Bears live in woods everywhere,
But if you should see one, take care.
They're not nice or funny
When they're eating honey.
They'd much rather swat you than share!

But You're Not A Bear!

The ostrich is large and quite grand,
But as friends go, he's not in demand.
For "Sorry"'s one word
Not said by this bird.
He just hides his head in the sand!

But You're Not An Ostrich!

Hyenas don't have much appeal.
They don't bother to see how you feel.
They laugh when you're mad.
They laugh when you're sad.
Hyenas are far from genteel!

But You're Not A Hyena!

Goats like to jump and to run.
They play through the day and have fun.
They're messy, not neat,
When they play and they eat,
And they never clean up when they're done!

But You're Not
A Goat!

The kangaroo's fast and he's strong.
He hops up and down all day long.
Though he's not always right,
He'd much rather fight
Than ever admit that he's wrong!

But You're Not A Kangaroo!

Now children who live with their mothers,
Their fathers, their sisters and brothers,
Will find life is good
When they act as they should
And practice good manners with others!

Designed by Bob Pantelone
Type set in Souvenir